Garfield

Shove At First Sight

JIM DAVIS

RAVETTE PUBLISHING

First published by Ravette Publishing 1998
Reprinted 1999

Printed and bound in Great Britain
for Ravette Publishing Limited,
Unit 3, Tristar Centre,
Star Road, Partridge Green,
West Sussex RH13 8RA
by Cox & Wyman Ltd, Reading, Berkshire

ISBN 1 85304 990 5

JIM DAVIS 10-20

I'M PRACTICING LOOKING INNOCENT

GARFIELD, WOULD YOU HAPPEN TO KNOW WHO EMPTIED THE REFRIGERATOR?

WITH A FACE LIKE THIS?

JIM DAVIS 11-9

JIM DAVIS 12-8

© 1995 PAWS, INC./Distributed by Universal Press Syndicate

© 1995 PAWS, INC./Distributed by Universal Press Syndicate

PAT
PAT
PAT

THERE!

JIM DAVIS 2-6

TAP
TAP

JIM DAVIS 2-8

© 1996 PAWS, INC./Distributed by Universal Press Syndicate

OTHER GARFIELD BOOKS AVAILABLE

Pocket Books @ £2.99 each   ISBN

Flying High	1 85304 043 6
A Gift For You	1 85304 190 4
The Gladiator	1 85304 941 7
Going Places	1 85304 242 0
Great Impressions	1 85304 191 2
Hangs On	1 85304 784 8
Happy Landings	1 85304 105 X
Here We Go Again	0 948456 10 8
In The Pink	0 948456 67 1
In Training	1 85304 785 6
The Irresistible	1 85304 940 9
Just Good Friends	0 948456 68 X
Le Magnifique!	1 85304 243 9
Let's Party	1 85304 906 9
On The Right Track	1 85304 907 7
On Top Of The World	1 85304 104 1
Pick Of The Bunch	1 85304 258 7
The Reluctant Romeo	1 85304 391 5
Says It With Flowers	1 85304 316 8
Strikes Again	0 906710 62 6
To Eat Or Not To Eat	1 85304 991 3
Wave Rebel	1 85304 317 6
With Love From Me To You	1 85304 392 3

Theme Books @ £3.99 each

Guide to Behaving Badly	1 85304 892 5
Guide to Healthy Living	1 85304 972 7
Guide to Insults	1 85304 895 X
Guide to Pigging Out	1 85304 893 3
Guide to Romance	1 85304 894 1
Guide to Successful Living	1 85304 973 5

Classics @ £4.99 each · ISBN
Volume One · 1 85304 970 0
Volume Two · 1 85304 971 9

Miscellaneous
Garfield Treasury · £9.99 · 1 85304 975 1

Garfield Address & Birthday · 1 85304 918 2
Book Gift Set · £7.99 inc VAT

Garfield 21st Birthday · 1 85304 995 6
Celebration Book · £9.99
(available May '99)

All Garfield books are available at your local bookshop or from the address below. Just tick the titles required and send the form with your remittance to:-

B.B.C.S., P.O. BOX 941, HULL, NORTH HUMBERSIDE HU1 3YQ
24 Hour Telephone Credit Card Line 01482 224626
Prices and availability are subject to change without notice.

Please enclose a cheque or postal order made payable to B.B.C.S. to the value of the cover price of the book and allow the following for postage and packing:

U.K. & B.F.P.O.: £1.00 for the first book and 50p for each additional book to a maximum of £3.50.

Overseas & Eire: £2.00 for the first book, £1.00 for the second and 50p for each additional book.

BLOCK CAPITALS PLEASE

Name ....

Address..

....

....

Cards accepted: Mastercard and Visa

Expiry Date ....Signature ....